SERMON NOTES

FOR TEENS

....

This book is dedicated to the teens at
First Baptist Church of Rochester, Michigan.

May you continue to grow in your knowledge
and love of our Lord Jesus Christ.

....

ISBN: 978-0-9859876-1-9

Printed in the United State of America

18 17 16 15 14 13   1 2 3 4

Published by:

truthsteps
PUBLISHING

Truth Steps Publishing, LLC
Rochester Hills, Michigan
TruthStepsPublishing.com

Design: Darrin Joiner

For more helpful resources
visit our online store:

www.truthstepspublishing.com/store

CONTENTS

NOTE TO TEENS

NOTE TAKING HAS MANY GREAT BENEFITS.

FIRST, it will help you keep your attention on the sermon. It can be so easy to be distracted by those around us. Even our own thoughts can take our focus away from the message of God's Word.

SECONDLY, taking notes will help you remember the message. The purpose of the sermon is to help you grow in your relationship with the Lord. If you can't remember any of the message beyond the church doors, you can't expect to grow spiritually.

A **THIRD** benefit of note taking, especially through a variety of methods, is the developing of a discerning ear (the ability to recognize God's Word when you hear it). It is up to you to know that your pastor is preaching the Word of God and not his own opinion, regardless of how Biblical it may sound (Acts 17:10-17).

Using Sermon Notes for Teens will help you keep your notes together and organized so you can have easy access to review your notes at any time. Keep it with your Bible so you are always ready.

Though Sermon Notes for Teens provides a variety in the things you listen for and write down, none will detract from your ability to hear and apply the message God has for you.

Each section begins with an instruction page on how to most effectively use that sermon note page. You should occasionally review the instructions so you can make sure you are gaining the most benefit from each note taking method.

> Don't be discouraged if the note taking sheet you've chosen doesn't seem to be working for that particular sermon. This happens from time to time. Just keep trying!
>
> May you continue to grow in the Lord as you hear His Word, apply it to your heart, and live it out through your daily life.

SERMON OUTLINE

To identify the sermon outline, first listen for the main topic or theme of the sermon. This can usually be determined within the introduction or first few minutes of the sermon.

The outline points will build upon or point back to the main topic of the sermon. Most often there are 3 to 5 main outline points. Be sure to include supporting Scripture references for each point when possible.

With practice, you will be able to more quickly and accurately identify the sermon outline. Over time, you will become more familiar with your pastor's sermon style. This will help you to easily figure out the sermon outline.

The Sermon Outline notes page (Part 2) provides space for writing additional notes on each sermon point.

Finish up by writing a specific application for yourself. To come up with an application, think of ways the message can help you grow spiritually or help you during the week with friends, school, teachers, family, etc.

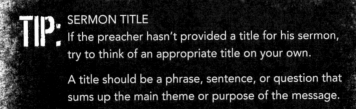

TIP: SERMON TITLE
If the preacher hasn't provided a title for his sermon, try to think of an appropriate title on your own.

A title should be a phrase, sentence, or question that sums up the main theme or purpose of the message.

SERMON OUTLINE PART 1

Write the main points of the sermon. Include supporting Scripture.

1) ....
....
....
....

2) ....
....
....
....

3) ....
....
....
....

4) ....
....
....
....

5) ....
....
....
....
....

SERMON OUTLINE PART 2

Date: ....

Scripture Text: ....

Sermon Title: ....

....

Sermon Notes: ....

....

....

....

....

....

....

....

....

....

....

....

....

....

Application: ....

....

....

....

....

SERMON OUTLINE PART 1

Write the main points of the sermon. Include supporting Scripture.

1) ....
....
....
....
....

2) ....
....
....
....

3) ....
....
....
....

4) ....
....
....
....

5) ....
....
....
....
....

SERMON OUTLINE PART 2

Date:
....

Scripture Text:
....

Sermon Title:
....

Sermon Notes:
....

....

....

....

....

....

....

....

....

....

....

....

....

....

Application:
....

....

....

....

....

SERMON OUTLINE PART 1

Write the main points of the sermon. Include supporting Scripture.

1) ....
....
....
....
....

2) ....
....
....
....

3) ....
....
....
....

4) ....
....
....
....

5) ....
....
....
....
....

SERMON OUTLINE PART 2

Date: ....

Scripture Text: ....

Sermon Title: ....

....

Sermon Notes: ....

....

....

....

....

....

....

....

....

....

....

....

....

....

....

....

Application: ....

....

....

....

....

11

SERMON OUTLINE PART 1

Write the main points of the sermon. Include supporting Scripture.

1) ....

....

....

....

2) ....

....

....

....

3) ....

....

....

....

4) ....

....

....

....

5) ....

....

....

....

....

SERMON OUTLINE PART 2

Date: ....

Scripture Text: ....

Sermon Title: ....

....

Sermon Notes:

....

....

....

....

....

....

....

....

....

....

....

....

....

....

....

....

....

....

Application: ....

....

....

....

....

....

SERMON OUTLINE PART 1

Write the main points of the sermon. Include supporting Scripture.

1) ....
....
....
....
....

2) ....
....
....
....

3) ....
....
....
....

4) ....
....
....
....

5) ....
....
....
....
....

SERMON OUTLINE PART 2

Date:
....

Scripture Text:
....

Sermon Title:
....

....

Sermon Notes:
....

....

....

....

....

....

....

....

....

....

....

....

....

....

....

Application:
....

....

....

....

....

SERMON OUTLINE PART 1

Write the main points of the sermon. Include supporting Scripture.

1) ....
....
....
....
....

2) ....
....
....
....
....

3) ....
....
....
....

4) ....
....
....
....

5) ....
....
....
....
....

SERMON OUTLINE PART 2

Date: ....

Scripture Text: ....

Sermon Title: ....

....

Sermon Notes: ....

....

....

....

....

....

....

....

....

....

....

....

....

....

....

....

....

Application: ....

....

....

....

....

....

SERMON OUTLINE PART 1

Write the main points of the sermon. Include supporting Scripture.

1) ....
....
....
....
....

2) ....
....
....
....

3) ....
....
....
....

4) ....
....
....
....

5) ....
....
....
....
....

SERMON OUTLINE PART 2

Date:
....

Scripture Text:
....

Sermon Title:
....

....

Sermon Notes:
....

....

....

....

....

....

....

....

....

....

....

....

....

....

....

....

Application:
....

....

....

....

....

SERMON OUTLINE PART 1

Write the main points of the sermon. Include supporting Scripture.

1) ....

....

....

....

2) ....

....

....

....

3) ....

....

....

....

4) ....

....

....

....

5) ....

....

....

....

....

SERMON OUTLINE PART 2

Date: ....

Scripture Text: ....

Sermon Title: ....

....

Sermon Notes: ....

....

....

....

....

....

....

....

....

....

....

....

....

....

....

....

....

....

Application: ....

....

....

....

....

....

SERMON OUTLINE PART 1

Write the main points of the sermon. Include supporting Scripture.

1) ....

....

....

....

....

2) ....

....

....

....

....

3) ....

....

....

....

4) ....

....

....

....

5) ....

....

....

....

....

SERMON OUTLINE PART 2

Date: ....

Scripture Text: ....

Sermon Title: ....

....

Sermon Notes:
....

....

....

....

....

....

....

....

....

....

....

....

....

....

....

....

....

....

....

Application: ....

....

....

....

....

....

SERMON OUTLINE PART 1

Write the main points of the sermon. Include supporting Scripture.

1) ....
....
....
....
....

2) ....
....
....
....
....

3) ....
....
....
....
....

4) ....
....
....
....
....

5) ....
....
....
....
....
....

SERMON OUTLINE PART 2

Date:
....

Scripture Text:
....

Sermon Title:
....

....

Sermon Notes:
....

....

....

....

....

....

....

....

....

....

....

....

....

....

....

....

Application:
....

....

....

....

....

SERMON OUTLINE PART 1

Write the main points of the sermon. Include supporting Scripture.

1) ....
....
....
....
....

2) ....
....
....
....

3) ....
....
....
....

4) ....
....
....
....

5) ....
....
....
....
....

SERMON OUTLINE PART 2

Date: ....

Scripture Text: ....

Sermon Title: ....

....

Sermon Notes: ....

....

....

....

....

....

....

....

....

....

....

....

....

....

....

....

....

Application: ....

....

....

....

....

SERMON OUTLINE PART 1

Write the main points of the sermon. Include supporting Scripture.

1) ....
....
....
....
....

2) ....
....
....
....

3) ....
....
....
....

4) ....
....
....
....

5) ....
....
....
....
....

SERMON OUTLINE PART 2

Date:
....

Scripture Text:
....

Sermon Title:
....

....

Sermon Notes:
....

....

....

....

....

....

....

....

....

....

....

....

....

....

....

....

Application:
....

....

....

....

....

SERMON OUTLINE PART 1

Write the main points of the sermon. Include supporting Scripture.

1) ....
....
....
....

2) ....
....
....
....

3) ....
....
....
....

4) ....
....
....
....

5) ....
....
....
....
....

SERMON OUTLINE PART 2

Date: ....

Scripture Text: ....

Sermon Title: ....

....

Sermon Notes: ....

....

....

....

....

....

....

....

....

....

....

....

....

....

....

Application: ....

....

....

....

....

....

SERMON OUTLINE PART 1

Write the main points of the sermon. Include supporting Scripture.

1) ....
....
....
....
....

2) ....
....
....
....

3) ....
....
....
....

4) ....
....
....
....

5) ....
....
....
....
....

SERMON OUTLINE PART 2

Date: ....

Scripture Text: ....

Sermon Title: ....

....

Sermon Notes: ....

....

....

....

....

....

....

....

....

....

....

....

....

....

....

....

....

Application: ....

....

....

....

....

....

SERMON ILLUSTRATOR

Visualize the sermon by drawing pictures of several of the main sermon points. Be creative and put your imagination to work.

You don't have to be an artist to enjoy and benefit from this type of note taking. Visualizing the main ideas of the sermon can help you to remember and apply the sermon.

The Sermon Illustrator notes page (Part 2) provides the space needed for written notes. Be sure to write the date and main Scripture text. Near the end of the sermon, write a sentence or two on how the sermon applies to you.

Finish your notes by giving a title to the sermon. The title should be a phrase, sentence, or question that sums up the main theme or purpose of the sermon.

TIP: Some sermons lend themselves to this method more than others. Don't be discouraged if at times you find Sermon Illustrator is not working for you. Simply switch over to another note taking sheet and come back to this one for a different sermon.

SERMON ILLUSTRATOR PART 1

Illustrate the main points of the sermon.

SERMON ILLUSTRATOR PART 2

Date: ....

Scripture Text: ....

Sermon Title: ....

....

Sermon Notes: ....

....

....

....

....

....

....

....

....

....

....

....

....

....

....

....

....

....

....

Application: ....

....

....

....

....

SERMON ILLUSTRATOR PART 1

Illustrate the main points of the sermon.

SERMON ILLUSTRATOR PART 2

Date:

Scripture Text:

Sermon Title:

Sermon Notes:

Application:

SERMON ILLUSTRATOR PART 1

Illustrate the main points of the sermon.

....

....

....

....

SERMON ILLUSTRATOR PART 2

Date:
....

Scripture Text:
....

Sermon Title:
....

....

Sermon Notes:
....

....

....

....

....

....

....

....

....

....

....

....

....

....

....

....

....

....

....

Application:
....

....

....

....

....

....

SERMON ILLUSTRATOR PART 1

Illustrate the main points of the sermon.

....

....

....

....

SERMON ILLUSTRATOR PART 2

Date:
....
Scripture Text:
....
Sermon Title:
....
....
Sermon Notes:
....
....
....
....
....
....
....
....
....
....
....
....
....
....
....
....
....
....
....
Application:
....
....
....
....
....

SERMON ILLUSTRATOR PART 1

Illustrate the main points of the sermon.

SERMON ILLUSTRATOR PART 2

Date:

Scripture Text:

Sermon Title:

Sermon Notes:

Application:

SERMON ILLUSTRATOR PART 1

Illustrate the main points of the sermon.

SERMON ILLUSTRATOR PART 2

Date:
....
Scripture Text:
....
Sermon Title:
....

Sermon Notes:
....
....
....
....
....
....
....
....
....
....
....
....
....
....
....
....
....
....
....

Application:
....
....
....
....
....

SERMON ILLUSTRATOR PART 1

Illustrate the main points of the sermon.

SERMON ILLUSTRATOR PART 2

Date:
....

Scripture Text:
....

Sermon Title:
....
....

Sermon Notes:
....

....

....

....

....

....

....

....

....

....

....

....

....

....

....

Application:
....

....

....

....

....

SERMON ILLUSTRATOR PART 1

Illustrate the main points of the sermon.

SERMON ILLUSTRATOR PART 2

Date:
....

Scripture Text:
....

Sermon Title:
....

....

Sermon Notes:
....

....

....

....

....

....

....

....

....

....

....

....

....

....

....

....

....

....

Application:
....

....

....

....

....

SERMON ILLUSTRATOR PART 1

Illustrate the main points of the sermon.

....

....

....

....

SERMON ILLUSTRATOR PART 2

Date:
....

Scripture Text:
....

Sermon Title:
....

....

Sermon Notes:
....

....

....

....

....

....

....

....

....

....

....

....

....

....

....

....

....

....

....

Application:
....

....

....

....

....

SERMON ILLUSTRATOR PART 1

Illustrate the main points of the sermon.

....

....

....

....

SERMON ILLUSTRATOR PART 2

Date: ....

Scripture Text: ....

Sermon Title: ....

....

Sermon Notes: ....

....

....

....

....

....

....

....

....

....

....

....

....

....

....

....

....

....

....

Application: ....

....

....

....

....

....

SERMON ILLUSTRATOR PART 1

Illustrate the main points of the sermon.

SERMON ILLUSTRATOR PART 2

Date:
....

Scripture Text:
....

Sermon Title:
....

....

Sermon Notes:
....

....

....

....

....

....

....

....

....

....

....

....

....

....

....

....

....

Application:
....

....

....

....

....

....

SERMON ILLUSTRATOR PART 1

Illustrate the main points of the sermon.

....

....

....

....

SERMON ILLUSTRATOR PART 2

Date:
....

Scripture Text:
....

Sermon Title:
....

Sermon Notes:
....
....
....
....
....
....
....
....
....
....
....
....
....
....
....
....
....

Application:
....
....
....
....
....

SERMON ILLUSTRATOR PART 1

Illustrate the main points of the sermon.

....

....

....

....

SERMON ILLUSTRATOR PART 2

Date:
....

Scripture Text:
....

Sermon Title:
....

....

Sermon Notes:
....

....

....

....

....

....

....

....

....

....

....

....

....

....

....

....

Application:
....

....

....

....

....

....

SERMON ILLUSTRATOR PART 1

Illustrate the main points of the sermon.

....

....

....

....

SERMON ILLUSTRATOR PART 2

Date:
....

Scripture Text:
....

Sermon Title:
....

....

Sermon Notes:
....

....

....

....

....

....

....

....

....

....

....

....

....

....

....

....

....

....

....

....

Application:
....

....

....

....

....

ILLUSTRATION INVESTIGATION

Preachers sometimes use real-life illustrations or stories to reinforce a point they are trying to make. However, too often it is easy to listen intently to the story and then mentally check out when the story ends.

Using this form will help keep you attentive by requiring you to identify the purpose of each real-life story.

In the space provided, write a brief summary or title for the illustration or story. You will then identify the purpose of the story by listening for what connection it had with the sermon. What sermon point or idea was the preacher emphasizing?

The Illustration Investigation notes page (Part 2) provides space for writing additional notes.

Finish your note taking by including a title for the sermon and a personal application.

TIP: WORD TO KNOW:

Application: A specific and practical way you can live out the message from God's Word.

A good application should clearly state how you can grow spiritually or how you can live more Christ-like in your relationships with friends, family, authority, strangers, or acquaintances.

Try to be as specific as possible in how you can apply the message.

ILLUSTRATION INVESTIGATION PART 1

Briefly summarize the real-life illustration or story told by the preacher. Identify what point or idea of the sermon is being emphasized.

Story summary:

....

....

....

Point of this story:

....

....

....

Story summary:

....

....

....

Point of this story:

....

....

....

Story summary:

....

....

....

Point of this story:

....

....

....

....

ILLUSTRATION INVESTIGATION PART 2

Date:

Scripture Text:

Sermon Title:

Sermon Notes:

Application:

ILLUSTRATION INVESTIGATION PART 1

Briefly summarize the real-life illustration or story told by the preacher. Identify what point or idea of the sermon is being emphasized.

Story summary:

....

....

....

Point of this story:

....

....

....

Story summary:

....

....

....

Point of this story:

....

....

....

Story summary:

....

....

....

Point of this story:

....

....

....

....

Date: ....

Scripture Text: ....

Sermon Title: ....

....

Sermon Notes: ....

....

....

....

....

....

....

....

....

....

....

....

....

....

Application: ....

....

....

....

....

....

ILLUSTRATION INVESTIGATION PART 1

Briefly summarize the real-life illustration or story told by the preacher. Identify what point or idea of the sermon is being emphasized.

Story summary:

....

....

....

Point of this story:

....

....

....

Story summary:

....

....

....

Point of this story:

....

....

....

Story summary:

....

....

....

Point of this story:

....

....

....

....

ILLUSTRATION INVESTIGATION PART 2

Date:

Scripture Text:

Sermon Title:

Sermon Notes:

Application:

ILLUSTRATION INVESTIGATION PART 1

Briefly summarize the real-life illustration or story told by the preacher.
Identify what point or idea of the sermon is being emphasized.

Story summary:

....

....

....

Point of this story:

....

....

....

Story summary:

....

....

....

Point of this story:

....

....

....

Story summary:

....

....

....

Point of this story:

....

....

....

....

Date:

Scripture Text:

Sermon Title:

Sermon Notes:

Application:

ILLUSTRATION INVESTIGATION PART 1

Briefly summarize the real-life illustration or story told by the preacher. Identify what point or idea of the sermon is being emphasized.

Story summary:

....

....

....

Point of this story:

....

....

....

Story summary:

....

....

....

Point of this story:

....

....

....

Story summary:

....

....

....

Point of this story:

....

....

....

ILLUSTRATION INVESTIGATION PART 2

Date:

Scripture Text:

Sermon Title:

Sermon Notes:

Application:

ILLUSTRATION INVESTIGATION PART 1

Briefly summarize the real-life illustration or story told by the preacher. Identify what point or idea of the sermon is being emphasized.

Story summary:

....

....

....

Point of this story:

....

....

....

Story summary:

....

....

....

Point of this story:

....

....

....

Story summary:

....

....

....

Point of this story:

....

....

....

....

ILLUSTRATION INVESTIGATION PART 2

Date:
....

Scripture Text:
....

Sermon Title:
....
....

Sermon Notes:
....

....

....

....

....

....

....

....

....

....

....

....

....

....

....

....

Application:
....

....

....

....

....

ILLUSTRATION INVESTIGATION PART 1

Briefly summarize the real-life illustration or story told by the preacher. Identify what point or idea of the sermon is being emphasized.

Story summary:

....

....

Point of this story:

....

....

Story summary:

....

....

Point of this story:

....

....

Story summary:

....

....

Point of this story:

....

....

....

Date:
....

Scripture Text:
....

Sermon Title:
....

....

Sermon Notes:
....

....

....

....

....

....

....

....

....

....

....

....

....

....

....

....

....

Application:
....

....

....

....

....

ILLUSTRATION INVESTIGATION PART 1

Briefly summarize the real-life illustration or story told by the preacher.
Identify what point or idea of the sermon is being emphasized.

Story summary:
....
....
....

Point of this story:
....
....
....

Story summary:
....
....
....

Point of this story:
....
....
....

Story summary:
....
....
....

Point of this story:
....
....
....

ILLUSTRATION INVESTIGATION PART 2

Date:
....

Scripture Text:
....

Sermon Title:
....

....

Sermon Notes:
....

....

....

....

....

....

....

....

....

....

....

....

....

....

Application:
....

....

....

....

....

ILLUSTRATION INVESTIGATION PART 1

Briefly summarize the real-life illustration or story told by the preacher. Identify what point or idea of the sermon is being emphasized.

Story summary:

....

....

....

Point of this story:

....

....

....

Story summary:

....

....

....

Point of this story:

....

....

....

Story summary:

....

....

....

Point of this story:

....

....

....

....

Date:
....

Scripture Text:
....

Sermon Title:
....

....

Sermon Notes:
....

....

....

....

....

....

....

....

....

....

....

....

....

....

....

....

Application:
....

....

....

....

....

ILLUSTRATION INVESTIGATION PART 1

Briefly summarize the real-life illustration or story told by the preacher. Identify what point or idea of the sermon is being emphasized.

Story summary:
....
....
....

Point of this story:
....
....
....

Story summary:
....
....
....

Point of this story:
....
....
....

Story summary:
....
....
....

Point of this story:
....
....
....

ILLUSTRATION INVESTIGATION PART 2

Date:
....

Scripture Text:
....

Sermon Title:
....

....

Sermon Notes:
....

....

....

....

....

....

....

....

....

....

....

....

....

....

....

....

Application:
....

....

....

....

....

ILLUSTRATION INVESTIGATION PART 1

Briefly summarize the real-life illustration or story told by the preacher. Identify what point or idea of the sermon is being emphasized.

Story summary:

....

....

....

Point of this story:

....

....

....

Story summary:

....

....

....

Point of this story:

....

....

....

Story summary:

....

....

....

Point of this story:

....

....

....

....

ILLUSTRATION INVESTIGATION PART 2

Date:

Scripture Text:

Sermon Title:

Sermon Notes:

Application:

ILLUSTRATION INVESTIGATION PART 1

Briefly summarize the real-life illustration or story told by the preacher. Identify what point or idea of the sermon is being emphasized.

Story summary:

....

....

....

Point of this story:

....

....

....

Story summary:

....

....

....

Point of this story:

....

....

....

Story summary:

....

....

....

Point of this story:

....

....

....

....

ILLUSTRATION INVESTIGATION PART 2

Date:
....

Scripture Text:
....

Sermon Title:
....

....

Sermon Notes:
....

....

....

....

....

....

....

....

....

....

....

....

....

....

....

....

Application:
....

....

....

....

....

ILLUSTRATION INVESTIGATION PART 1

Briefly summarize the real-life illustration or story told by the preacher. Identify what point or idea of the sermon is being emphasized.

Story summary:

....

....

....

Point of this story:

....

....

Story summary:

....

....

....

Point of this story:

....

....

Story summary:

....

....

....

Point of this story:

....

....

....

ILLUSTRATION INVESTIGATION PART 2

Date:

Scripture Text:

Sermon Title:

Sermon Notes:

Application:

ILLUSTRATION INVESTIGATION PART 1

Briefly summarize the real-life illustration or story told by the preacher. Identify what point or idea of the sermon is being emphasized.

Story summary:
....
....
....
....

Point of this story:
....
....
....

Story summary:
....
....
....

Point of this story:
....
....
....

Story summary:
....
....
....

Point of this story:
....
....
....
....

ILLUSTRATION INVESTIGATION PART 2

Date:
....

Scripture Text:
....

Sermon Title:
....

....

Sermon Notes:
....

....

....

....

....

....

....

....

....

....

....

....

....

....

....

Application:
....

....

....

....

....

ill it affect me? YES!

in the field; the one shall be taken, and
atthew 24:40) If you miss the rapture,
t behind to go through the Great
as a non-believer, you will end up in hell

an it be true? JESUS SAID SO!

again, and receive you unto myself; that
here ye may be also." (John 14:3b) Jesus
ot lie. He promised to come again, and He
who are ready - the saved.

uld I do? REPENT, BELIEVE, BE SAVED!

erefore, and be converted, that your sins may
ut," (Acts 3:19a) "...Believe on the Lord Jesus
thou shalt be saved, and thy house." (Acts
r by grace are ye saved through faith; and that
selves: it is the gift of God:" (Ephesians 2:8)

ave decided to trust Jesus Christ as your Saviour
reading this tract, please write and let us know.

Words of Truth
Tract Ministry
PO Box 86
Middletown, PA 17057

Zip _____

Age _____

FELLOWSHIP TRACT LEAGUE
P.O. BOX 164 • LEBANON, OH 45036 • mail@fellowshiptractleague.org
www.fellowshiptractleague.org © Tract 135
All tracts free as the Lord provides. Not to be sold.

THE SECOND COMING
Surely I Come Quickly. Rev. 22:20

WHERE DID
EVERYBODY GO?

WHAT IS
HAPPENING?

WHY AM I
LEFT HERE?

IS THERE
ANY HOPE?

The questions on the cover are some you might be asking if you miss the first phase of the Second Coming of Jesus Christ to the earth, called the rapture!

WHAT IS THE RAPTURE?

This is when Jesus Christ comes for His saints, those who have by faith completely trusted the eternity of their souls to His saving power with nothing else added. *"For the Lord himself shall descend from heaven with a shout, with the voice of the archangel, and with the trump of God: and the dead in Christ shall rise first: Then we which are alive and remain shall be caught up together with them in the clouds, to meet the Lord in the air: and so shall we ever be with the Lord."* (1 Thessalonians 4:16-17)

WILL YOU BE LEFT BEHIND?

Those left behind will cry out for help and comfort. Questions will arise in every heart. Where did the "Christians" go? One man, Satan's soul-incarnate, the antichrist, will have all the answers. *"Even him, whose coming is after the working of Satan with all power and signs and lying wonders, And with all deceivableness of unrighteousness in them that perish; because they received not the love of the truth, that they might be saved. And for this cause God shall send them strong delusion, that they should believe a lie: That they all might be damned who believed not the truth, but had pleasure in unrighteousness."* (2 Thessalonians 2:9-12)

THE GREAT TRIBULATION

Peace will reign for 3 1/2 years. Then, in this time called the Great Trib...

judgment will
emissaries, the
wreak havoc on

Revelation 16
out on a God-fors
Putrifying painful so
filled with blood, and
plague man and beas
blasphemous man, and
of full darkness, as men
Euphrates River is drie
earthquakes, tremendous t
huge hail stones that pou
inhabitants. "It is done," thu
wrath is satisfied.

THE SECOND

Then the second phase of
transpires! *"...the coming of our*
his saints." (1 Thessalonians 3:13b)
the armies of the antichrist. The Lor
for 1000 years! You say, "I just canno
many questions." Let's allow God's W
for you.

When will the rapture take pla

"...for in such an hour as ye think not
cometh." (Matthew 24:44b) *"But of that*
knoweth no man, no, not the angels of he
Father only." (Matthew 24:36)

W

"Then shall two be
the other left." (N
you will be le
Tribulation. Then
for all eternity.

How

"... I will come
where I am, t
Christ would
will for those

What sho
"Repent ye t
be blotted o
Christ, and
16:31b) "F
not of your

If you
afte

Name

Address

City

State

DIGGING DEEPER

The goal of preaching God's Word is for the truth to spiritually nourish God's people. The sermon must line up with God's intended meaning.

To accomplish this, many preachers use a method often referred to as expository preaching (see below). This method helps the preacher to deliver a message based on God's Word and not his own opinion.

Don't be discouraged if you find you are not able to fill in every section on this form. The more you listen to expository preaching, the easier this form will be to complete.

INSTRUCTIONS:
Note any **historical or cultural background** of the times in which the Scripture passage was written.

What was life like at that time?

What events were taking place at that point in history?

The **context of surrounding Scripture** reveals how the selected passage relates to the chapter or book in which it is contained.

What group of people was the author writing to or about?

What is the theme or purpose of the passage?

If any **Hebrew or Greek definitions** are mentioned, note those as well. Phonetic spelling is perfectly acceptable!

As the sermon progresses, truths should begin to emerge that are applicable to our present culture and time. Once these truths are identified, be sure to **write an application** specific to your life.

TIP: WORDS TO KNOW:

Exposition: the setting forth of meaning or purpose.

Expository preaching: discovering the original intended meaning or purpose of a given passage of Scripture by digging into the context (surrounding Scripture) as well as the historical and cultural background.

DIGGING DEEPER PART 1

Listen for how the preacher digs into the Scripture text and pulls out the meaning and application it has for us today.

DIGGING INTO THE TEXT:
Historical background of the time and place:

....

....

....

Context of surrounding Scripture:

....

....

....

Hebrew/Greek definitions:

....

....

....

PULLING OUT TIMELESS PRINCIPLES:
What truths emerged from the original meaning that go beyond time & culture?

....

....

....

How does this directly apply to you?

....

....

....

....

DIGGING DEEPER PART 2

Date: ....

Scripture Text: ....

Sermon Title: ....

....

Sermon Notes: ....

....

....

....

....

....

....

....

....

....

....

....

....

....

....

....

Application: ....

....

....

....

....

....

DIGGING DEEPER PART 1

Listen for how the preacher digs into the Scripture text and pulls out the meaning and application it has for us today.

DIGGING INTO THE TEXT:

Historical background of the time and place:

....

....

....

Context of surrounding Scripture:

....

....

....

Hebrew/Greek definitions:

....

....

....

PULLING OUT TIMELESS PRINCIPLES:

What truths emerged from the original meaning that go beyond time & culture?

....

....

....

How does this directly apply to you?

....

....

....

....

DIGGING DEEPER PART 2

Date:
....

Scripture Text:
....

Sermon Title:
....

....

Sermon Notes:
....

....

....

....

....

....

....

....

....

....

....

....

....

....

Application:
....

....

....

....

....

DIGGING DEEPER PART 1

Listen for how the preacher digs into the Scripture text and pulls out the meaning and application it has for us today.

DIGGING INTO THE TEXT:

Historical background of the time and place:

....

....

....

Context of surrounding Scripture:

....

....

....

Hebrew/Greek definitions:

....

....

....

PULLING OUT TIMELESS PRINCIPLES:

What truths emerged from the original meaning that go beyond time & culture?

....

....

....

How does this directly apply to you?

....

....

....

....

DIGGING DEEPER PART 2

Date:
....

Scripture Text:
....

Sermon Title:
....

....

Sermon Notes:
....

....

....

....

....

....

....

....

....

....

....

....

....

....

....

....

....

Application:
....

....

....

....

....

....

DIGGING DEEPER PART 1

Listen for how the preacher digs into the Scripture text and pulls out the meaning and application it has for us today.

DIGGING INTO THE TEXT:

Historical background of the time and place:

....

....

....

Context of surrounding Scripture:

....

....

....

Hebrew/Greek definitions:

....

....

....

PULLING OUT TIMELESS PRINCIPLES:

What truths emerged from the original meaning that go beyond time & culture?

....

....

....

....

How does this directly apply to you?

....

....

....

....

....

DIGGING DEEPER PART 2

Date:
....

Scripture Text:
....

Sermon Title:
....
....

Sermon Notes:
....
....
....
....
....
....
....
....
....
....
....
....
....
....
....
....

Application:
....
....
....
....
....

DIGGING DEEPER PART 1

Listen for how the preacher digs into the Scripture text and pulls out the meaning and application it has for us today.

DIGGING INTO THE TEXT:

Historical background of the time and place:

....

....

....

Context of surrounding Scripture:

....

....

....

Hebrew/Greek definitions:

....

....

....

PULLING OUT TIMELESS PRINCIPLES:

What truths emerged from the original meaning that go beyond time & culture?

....

....

....

How does this directly apply to you?

....

....

....

....

DIGGING DEEPER PART 2

Date:
....

Scripture Text:
....

Sermon Title:
....

....

Sermon Notes:
....

....

....

....

....

....

....

....

....

....

....

....

....

....

....

....

....

Application:
....

....

....

....

....

DIGGING DEEPER PART 1

Listen for how the preacher digs into the Scripture text and pulls out the meaning and application it has for us today.

DIGGING INTO THE TEXT:
Historical background of the time and place:
....
....
....
....

Context of surrounding Scripture:
....
....
....
....

Hebrew/Greek definitions:
....
....
....

PULLING OUT TIMELESS PRINCIPLES:
What truths emerged from the original meaning that go beyond time & culture?
....
....
....
....

How does this directly apply to you?
....
....
....
....
....

DIGGING DEEPER PART 2

Date:

Scripture Text:

Sermon Title:

Sermon Notes:

Application:

DIGGING DEEPER PART 1

Listen for how the preacher digs into the Scripture text and pulls out the meaning and application it has for us today.

DIGGING INTO THE TEXT:

Historical background of the time and place:

....

....

....

Context of surrounding Scripture:

....

....

....

Hebrew/Greek definitions:

....

....

....

PULLING OUT TIMELESS PRINCIPLES:

What truths emerged from the original meaning that go beyond time & culture?

....

....

....

How does this directly apply to you?

....

....

....

....

DIGGING DEEPER PART 2

Date:
....

Scripture Text:
....

Sermon Title:
....
....

Sermon Notes:
....
....
....
....
....
....
....
....
....
....
....
....
....
....
....
....
....
....

Application:
....
....
....
....
....

DIGGING DEEPER PART 1

Listen for how the preacher digs into the Scripture text and pulls out the meaning and application it has for us today.

DIGGING INTO THE TEXT:

Historical background of the time and place:

....

....

....

Context of surrounding Scripture:

....

....

....

Hebrew/Greek definitions:

....

....

....

PULLING OUT TIMELESS PRINCIPLES:

What truths emerged from the original meaning that go beyond time & culture?

....

....

....

How does this directly apply to you?

....

....

....

....

....

DIGGING DEEPER PART 2

Date:
....

Scripture Text:
....

Sermon Title:
....

....

Sermon Notes:
....

....

....

....

....

....

....

....

....

....

....

....

....

....

....

....

....

Application:
....

....

....

....

....

DIGGING DEEPER PART 1

Listen for how the preacher digs into the Scripture text and pulls out the meaning and application it has for us today.

DIGGING INTO THE TEXT:

Historical background of the time and place:

....

....

....

Context of surrounding Scripture:

....

....

....

Hebrew/Greek definitions:

....

....

....

PULLING OUT TIMELESS PRINCIPLES:

What truths emerged from the original meaning that go beyond time & culture?

....

....

....

How does this directly apply to you?

....

....

....

....

DIGGING DEEPER PART 2

Date:
....

Scripture Text:
....

Sermon Title:
....

....

Sermon Notes:
....

....

....

....

....

....

....

....

....

....

....

....

....

....

....

Application:
....

....

....

....

....

DIGGING DEEPER PART 1

Listen for how the preacher digs into the Scripture text and pulls out the meaning and application it has for us today.

DIGGING INTO THE TEXT:

Historical background of the time and place:

....

....

....

Context of surrounding Scripture:

....

....

....

Hebrew/Greek definitions:

....

....

....

PULLING OUT TIMELESS PRINCIPLES:

What truths emerged from the original meaning that go beyond time & culture?

....

....

....

....

How does this directly apply to you?

....

....

....

....

....

DIGGING DEEPER PART 2

Date: ....

Scripture Text: ....

Sermon Title: ....

....

Sermon Notes: ....

....

....

....

....

....

....

....

....

....

....

....

....

....

....

....

....

....

Application: ....

....

....

....

....

....

DIGGING DEEPER PART 1

Listen for how the preacher digs into the Scripture text and pulls out the meaning and application it has for us today.

DIGGING INTO THE TEXT:

Historical background of the time and place:

....

....

....

Context of surrounding Scripture:

....

....

....

Hebrew/Greek definitions:

....

....

....

PULLING OUT TIMELESS PRINCIPLES:

What truths emerged from the original meaning that go beyond time & culture?

....

....

....

How does this directly apply to you?

....

....

....

....

DIGGING DEEPER PART 2

Date: ....

Scripture Text: ....

Sermon Title: ....

....

Sermon Notes: ....

....

....

....

....

....

....

....

....

....

....

....

....

....

....

....

....

Application: ....

....

....

....

....

....

DIGGING DEEPER PART 1

Listen for how the preacher digs into the Scripture text and pulls out the meaning and application it has for us today.

DIGGING INTO THE TEXT:
Historical background of the time and place:
....
....
....

Context of surrounding Scripture:
....
....
....

Hebrew/Greek definitions:
....
....
....

PULLING OUT TIMELESS PRINCIPLES:
What truths emerged from the original meaning that go beyond time & culture?
....
....
....

How does this directly apply to you?
....
....
....
....

DIGGING DEEPER PART 2

Date:
....

Scripture Text:
....

Sermon Title:
....

....

Sermon Notes:
....

....

....

....

....

....

....

....

....

....

....

....

....

....

....

....

Application:
....

....

....

....

....

DIGGING DEEPER PART 1

Listen for how the preacher digs into the Scripture text and pulls out the meaning and application it has for us today.

DIGGING INTO THE TEXT:

Historical background of the time and place:

....

....

....

Context of surrounding Scripture:

....

....

....

Hebrew/Greek definitions:

....

....

....

PULLING OUT TIMELESS PRINCIPLES:

What truths emerged from the original meaning that go beyond time & culture?

....

....

....

How does this directly apply to you?

....

....

....

....

DIGGING DEEPER PART 2

Date:
....

Scripture Text:
....

Sermon Title:
....

....

Sermon Notes:
....

....

....

....

....

....

....

....

....

....

....

....

....

....

....

....

Application:
....

....

....

....

....

....

DIGGING DEEPER PART 1

Listen for how the preacher digs into the Scripture text and pulls out the meaning and application it has for us today.

DIGGING INTO THE TEXT:

Historical background of the time and place:

....

....

....

Context of surrounding Scripture:

....

....

....

Hebrew/Greek definitions:

....

....

....

PULLING OUT TIMELESS PRINCIPLES:

What truths emerged from the original meaning that go beyond time & culture?

....

....

....

How does this directly apply to you?

....

....

....

....

DIGGING DEEPER PART 2

Date:
....

Scripture Text:
....

Sermon Title:
....
....

Sermon Notes:
....
....
....
....
....
....
....
....
....
....
....
....
....
....
....
....
....

Application:
....
....
....
....
....

SERMON NOTES

This section of Sermon Notes is available so you can take notes however you like.

The lined pages can be used for writing the main points of an outline or more Illustration Investigations. The unlined pages can be used for more illustrating of sermons. You might even come up with your own creative methods for taking notes.

Remember to always write a specific application as well as an appropriate title.

IDEA: If you come up with a new idea for note taking, I would love for you to share it with me! You can contact me through TruthStepsPublishing.com

SERMON NOTES

Date:

Scripture Text:

Sermon Title:

Sermon Notes:

Application:

SERMON NOTES

Date:
....

Scripture Text:
....

Sermon Title:
....

Application:
....

....

....

....

....

SERMON NOTES

Date:
....

Scripture Text:
....

Sermon Title:
....

....

Sermon Notes:
....

....

....

....

....

....

....

....

....

....

....

....

....

....

....

Application:
....

....

....

....

....

SERMON NOTES

Date:

Scripture Text:

Sermon Title:

Application:

SERMON NOTES

Date:
....

Scripture Text:
....

Sermon Title:
....

....

Sermon Notes:
....

....

....

....

....

....

....

....

....

....

....

....

....

Application:
....

....

....

....

....

SERMON NOTES

Date: ....

Scripture Text: ....

Sermon Title: ....

Application: ....

....

....

....

....

....

SERMON NOTES

Date: ....

Scripture Text: ....

Sermon Title: ....

....

Sermon Notes: ....

....

....

....

....

....

....

....

....

....

....

....

....

....

Application: ....

....

....

....

....

SERMON NOTES

Date:
Scripture Text:
Sermon Title:

Application:

SERMON NOTES

Date:
....

Scripture Text:
....

Sermon Title:
....

....

Sermon Notes:
....

....

....

....

....

....

....

....

....

....

....

....

....

Application:
....

....

....

....

....

SERMON NOTES

Date:

Scripture Text:

Sermon Title:

Application:

SERMON NOTES

Date:
....

Scripture Text:
....

Sermon Title:
....

....

Sermon Notes:
....

....

....

....

....

....

....

....

....

....

....

....

....

....

Application:
....

....

....

....

....

SERMON NOTES

Date:

Scripture Text:

Sermon Title:

Application:

SERMON NOTES

Date:
....

Scripture Text:
....

Sermon Title:
....
....

Sermon Notes:
....
....
....
....
....
....
....
....
....
....
....
....

....
....
....

Application:
....
....
....
....
....

SERMON NOTES

Date: ....

Scripture Text: ....

Sermon Title: ....

Application: ....

....

....

....

....

....

SERMON NOTES

Date:
....

Scripture Text:
....

Sermon Title:
....
....

Sermon Notes:
....
....
....
....
....
....
....
....
....
....

....
....
....

Application:
....
....
....
....

SERMON NOTES

Date: ....

Scripture Text: ....

Sermon Title: ....

Application: ....

....

....

....

....

....

SERMON NOTES

Date:
....

Scripture Text:
....

Sermon Title:
....
....

Sermon Notes:
....
....
....
....
....
....
....
....
....
....

....
....
....
....

Application:
....
....
....
....
....

SERMON NOTES

Date:

Scripture Text:

Sermon Title:

Application:

SERMON NOTES

Date:

Scripture Text:

Sermon Title:

Sermon Notes:

Application:

SERMON NOTES

Date:

Scripture Text:

Sermon Title:

Application:

SERMON NOTES

Date:
....

Scripture Text:
....

Sermon Title:
....

....

Sermon Notes:
....

....

....

....

....

....

....

....

....

....

....

....

....

Application:
....

....

....

....

SERMON NOTES

Date:
....

Scripture Text:
....

Sermon Title:
....

Application:
....

....

....

....

....

SERMON NOTES

Date:
....

Scripture Text:
....

Sermon Title:
....

....

Sermon Notes:
....

....

....

....

....

....

....

....

....

....

....

....

....

....

....

Application:
....

....

....

....

....

SERMON NOTES

Date: ....

Scripture Text: ....

Sermon Title: ....

Application: ....

....

....

....

....

....

SERMON NOTES

Date:
....

Scripture Text:
....

Sermon Title:
....

....

Sermon Notes:
....

....

....

....

....

....

....

....

....

....

....

....

....

Application:
....

....

....

....

SERMON NOTES

Date:
....

Scripture Text:
....

Sermon Title:
....

Application:
....

....

....

....

....

....

SERMON NOTES

Date:
....

Scripture Text:
....

Sermon Title:
....
....

Sermon Notes:
....
....
....
....
....
....
....
....
....
....
....
....
....
....

Application:
....
....
....
....
....

SERMON NOTES

Date:

Scripture Text:

Sermon Title:

Application:

MISSIONARY MOMENTS

When I was growing up, I sometimes found it difficult to listen to guest missionary speakers. Their slides and stories all seemed to look and sound alike. That's probably because missionaries all have the same primary purpose to which they devote their lives: spreading the Gospel around the world.

Missionaries are people just like you and me. But as different as you probably are from me, so are the God-given gifts and experiences of each missionary.

Use the Missionary Moments pages to help you listen to a missionary presentation and discover the uniqueness of each.

MISSIONARY MOMENTS

Date:

Missionary Name:

Country serving in:

What is the main ministry?   ☐ church plant   ☐ education   ☐ medical

                             ☐ construction   ☐ special interest group

                             ☐ other

What are some specific ways the ministry is accomplished?

Specific prayer requests:

Scripture or devotional shared:

What interested you most about the missionary?

MISSIONARY MOMENTS

Date: ....

Missionary Name: ....

Country serving in: ....

What is the main ministry? ☐ church plant   ☐ education   ☐ medical

☐ construction   ☐ special interest group

☐ other   ....

What are some specific ways the ministry is accomplished? ....
....
....

Specific prayer requests: ....
....
....

Scripture or devotional shared: ....
....
....
....
....

What interested you most about the missionary? ....
....
....
....
....

MISSIONARY MOMENTS

Date:

Missionary Name:

Country serving in:

What is the main ministry?   ☐ church plant   ☐ education   ☐ medical

☐ construction   ☐ special interest group

☐ other

What are some specific ways the ministry is accomplished?

Specific prayer requests:

Scripture or devotional shared:

What interested you most about the missionary?

MISSIONARY MOMENTS

Date:
Missionary Name:
Country serving in:

What is the main ministry? ☐ church plant   ☐ education   ☐ medical
                            ☐ construction   ☐ special interest group
                            ☐ other   ....

What are some specific ways the ministry is accomplished?
....
....
....

Specific prayer requests:
....
....
....

Scripture or devotional shared:
....
....
....
....

What interested you most about the missionary?
....
....
....
....
....

MISSIONARY MOMENTS

Date:
....

Missionary Name:
....

Country serving in:
....

What is the main ministry?　☐ church plant　☐ education　☐ medical

☐ construction　☐ special interest group

☐ other ....

What are some specific ways the ministry is accomplished?
....
....
....

Specific prayer requests:
....
....
....

Scripture or devotional shared:
....
....
....
....

What interested you most about the missionary?
....
....
....
....

MISSIONARY MOMENTS

Date: ....

Missionary Name: ....

Country serving in: ....

What is the main ministry?　☐ church plant　☐ education　☐ medical

　　　　　　　　　　　　　　☐ construction　☐ special interest group

　　　　　　　　　　　　　　☐ other　...

What are some specific ways the ministry is accomplished? ....
....
....

Specific prayer requests: ....
....
....

Scripture or devotional shared: ....
....
....
....
....

What interested you most about the missionary? ....
....
....
....
....

MISSIONARY MOMENTS

Date:
Missionary Name:
Country serving in:

What is the main ministry?   ☐ church plant   ☐ education   ☐ medical

☐ construction   ☐ special interest group

☐ other

What are some specific ways the ministry is accomplished?

Specific prayer requests:

Scripture or devotional shared:

What interested you most about the missionary?

MISSIONARY MOMENTS

Date:

Missionary Name:

Country serving in:

What is the main ministry? ☐ church plant ☐ education ☐ medical

☐ construction ☐ special interest group

☐ other

What are some specific ways the ministry is accomplished?

Specific prayer requests:

Scripture or devotional shared:

What interested you most about the missionary?

MISSIONARY MOMENTS

Date:
....

Missionary Name:
....

Country serving in:
....

What is the main ministry? ☐ church plant   ☐ education   ☐ medical

☐ construction   ☐ special interest group

☐ other ....

What are some specific ways the ministry is accomplished?
....
....
....

Specific prayer requests:
....
....
....

Scripture or devotional shared:
....
....
....
....

What interested you most about the missionary?
....
....
....
....

MISSIONARY MOMENTS

Date: ....

Missionary Name: ....

Country serving in: ....

What is the main ministry?
☐ church plant ☐ education ☐ medical
☐ construction ☐ special interest group
☐ other ....

What are some specific ways the ministry is accomplished?
....
....
....

Specific prayer requests:
....
....
....

Scripture or devotional shared:
....
....
....
....

What interested you most about the missionary?
....
....
....
....

MISSIONARY MOMENTS

Date:

Missionary Name:

Country serving in:

What is the main ministry? ☐ church plant   ☐ education   ☐ medical

☐ construction   ☐ special interest group

☐ other

What are some specific ways the ministry is accomplished?

Specific prayer requests:

Scripture or devotional shared:

What interested you most about the missionary?

MISSIONARY MOMENTS

Date: ....

Missionary Name: ....

Country serving in: ....

What is the main ministry?   ☐ church plant   ☐ education   ☐ medical

☐ construction   ☐ special interest group

☐ other   ....

What are some specific ways the ministry is accomplished?
....
....
....

Specific prayer requests:
....
....
....

Scripture or devotional shared:
....
....
....
....

What interested you most about the missionary?
....
....
....
....

PRAYER MEETING

This section is useful for whenever you participate in a prayer meeting, whether in a large group or small.

If a devotional is given, **write the Scripture reference** along with a **few notes** about the message.

Write down answers to prayer. This will serve as a reminder that God hears and responds to our requests. Notice how the prayers were answered. Were they always answered in the way the person requested?

List a couple of your own personal requests. If you are comfortable, share them with the group so others can pray on your behalf.

Lastly, commit to praying for some of the requests of others. Write down ones that you would enjoy praying for in the days ahead. When these prayers are eventually answered, you will experience joy in having been a part of praying for them.

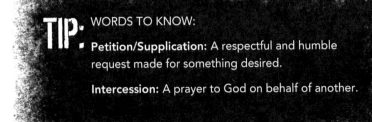

TIP: WORDS TO KNOW:

- **Petition/Supplication:** A respectful and humble request made for something desired.

- **Intercession:** A prayer to God on behalf of another.

PRAYER MEETING

Scripture/Devotional Notes:

Praise / Answered prayers:

My personal prayer requests:

Requests of others I would like to pray for:

PRAYER MEETING

Scripture/Devotional Notes:

Praise / Answered prayers:

My personal prayer requests:

Requests of others I would like to pray for:

PRAYER MEETING

Scripture/Devotional Notes:

Praise / Answered prayers:

My personal prayer requests:

Requests of others I would like to pray for:

PRAYER MEETING

Scripture/Devotional Notes:

Praise / Answered prayers:

My personal prayer requests:

Requests of others I would like to pray for:

PRAYER MEETING

Scripture/Devotional Notes:

Praise / Answered prayers:

My personal prayer requests:

Requests of others I would like to pray for:

PRAYER MEETING

Scripture/Devotional Notes:

Praise / Answered prayers:

My personal prayer requests:

Requests of others I would like to pray for:

PRAYER MEETING

Scripture/Devotional Notes:

Praise / Answered prayers:

My personal prayer requests:

Requests of others I would like to pray for:

PRAYER MEETING

Scripture/Devotional Notes:

Praise / Answered prayers:

My personal prayer requests:

Requests of others I would like to pray for:

PRAYER MEETING

Scripture/Devotional Notes:

Praise / Answered prayers:

My personal prayer requests:

Requests of others I would like to pray for:

PRAYER MEETING

Scripture/Devotional Notes:

Praise / Answered prayers:

My personal prayer requests:

Requests of others I would like to pray for:

PRAYER MEETING

Scripture/Devotional Notes:

Praise / Answered prayers:

My personal prayer requests:

Requests of others I would like to pray for:

PRAYER MEETING

Scripture/Devotional Notes:

Praise / Answered prayers:

My personal prayer requests:

Requests of others I would like to pray for:

LORD'S SUPPER

Regardless of how often your church practices the Lord's Supper (also known as Communion) or even how it is done, its purpose is always the same. Jesus said in Luke 22:19, "...do this in remembrance of me."

Paul makes it clear in 1 Corinthians 11 that this formal practice of remembrance needs to be done with an attitude of respect, seriousness, and care. It is not to be taken lightly.

When participating in the Lord's Supper, it is important to focus your thoughts on your relationship with Jesus Christ. You can do this by:

1) making certain your heart is in a right standing with Him, and

2) directing your mind to what Christ accomplished for you through His death and resurrection.

Use this Communion guide to help keep your mind and heart on Jesus.

TIP: WORDS TO KNOW:

Communion: Means to share or participate (as found in 1 Corinthians 10:16)

Eucharist: Greek word for giving thanks (as found in 1 Corinthians 11:24)

Lord's Table: Also referred to as the Lord's Supper (as found in 1 Corinthians. 11:20)

LORD'S SUPPER

Below are some thoughts and Scripture for you to think about and read during Communion, whether you are participating in it or not.

1) **CONFESSION** – Are there any sins you have not yet told God you are sorry for? Take a couple minutes to ask God to reveal anything in your heart that is not pleasing to Him. Then repent and ask forgiveness.

   "Search me, O God, and know my heart; test me and know my anxious thoughts. See if there is any offensive way in me, and lead me in the way everlasting." - **Psalm 139:23-24**

2) **REMEMBER** – Spend a few minutes reading about Christ's death, burial, resurrection, and last supper. Choose one of the Gospel accounts below.

	DEATH, BURIAL, RESURRECTION	LAST SUPPER
1.	Matthew 27:26 – 28:7	Matthew 26:26-30
2.	Mark 15:16 – 16:7	Mark 14:22-26
3.	Luke 23:26 – 24:8	Luke 22:14-20
4.	John 19:16 – 20:9	1 Corinthians 11:23-27

3) **PRAISE** – Spend the last few moments praising and thanking God for who He is. Below are listed a few great praise Psalms.

PSALM 93	PSALM 97
PSALM 94	PSALM 98
PSALM 95	PSALM 99
PSALM 96	PSALM 100

LORD'S SUPPER

Write your own thoughts and favorite Scripture appropriate for Communion.

....

....

....

....

....

....

....

....

....

....

....

....

....

....

....

....

....

....

....

....

....

....

....

....

....